**LEARNING
ACTIVITY
PACKET**

BASIC
PNEUMATICS

PNEUMATIC POWER SYSTEMS

BB834-BA01XEN

PNEUMATIC POWER SYSTEMS

INTRODUCTION

Pneumatic power technology is used to power machines in almost every manufacturing plant in the world. They have many unique features that have caused their use to continue to grow rapidly.

This learning system will explore the basic skills in pneumatic power. Each LAP will discuss how to connect and operate basic components and systems, read circuit diagrams, monitor system operation, and design circuits.

The Amatrol 850 Series hydraulic and pneumatic trainers will be used in learning these skills. These trainers are designed with real-world industrial components that allow actual circuit setup and operation testing.

This first pneumatic LAP will introduce pneumatic power by explaining how to use the pneumatic system to connect and operate pneumatic circuits safely. Additionally, it will discuss how pneumatic circuits are drawn using symbols, a necessity for anyone working with pneumatic equipment.

ITEMS NEEDED

Amatrol Supplied
    1   85-BP Basic Pneumatic Learning System

School Supplied
    1   Compressed Air Supply
    1   Screw Driver, small flat-head
         Paper Towels

SECOND EDITION, LAP 1, REV. B

Amatrol, AMNET, CIMSOFT, MCL, MINI-CIM, IST, ITC, VEST, and Technovate are trademarks or registered trademarks of Amatrol, Inc. All other brand and product names are trademarks or registered trademarks of their respective companies.

Amatrol,Inc., 2400 Centennial Blvd., Jeffersonville, IN 47130 USA, Ph 812-288-8285, FAX 812-283-1584 www.amatrol.com

TABLE OF CONTENTS

SEGMENT 1 INTRODUCTION TO PNEUMATICS... **4**
OBJECTIVE 1 Define pneumatics and give an application
OBJECTIVE 2 Describe the functions of basic components of a pneumatic system
    Activity 1 Pneumatic trainer
OBJECTIVE 3 Define pneumatic pressure and give its units of measurement
SKILL 1 Read a pneumatic pressure gauge
OBJECTIVE 4 Describe the function of a pneumatic schematic

SEGMENT 2 PNEUMATIC POWER.. **20**
OBJECTIVE 5 Explain six pneumatic safety rules
OBJECTIVE 6 Describe the function of a pressure regulator valve and give an application
OBJECTIVE 7 Describe the operation of a pressure regulator and give its schematic symbol
SKILL 2 Connect and adjust a pressure regulator
OBJECTIVE 8 Describe the function of an air filter
OBJECTIVE 9 Describe the operation of an air filter and give its schematic symbol
SKILL 3 Drain a pneumatic filter

SEGMENT 3 CIRCUIT CONNECTIONS.. **37**
OBJECTIVE 10 Describe the function of a pneumatic quick-connect fitting and give its schematic symbol
SKILL 4 Connect a pneumatic hose that uses quick-connect fittings
OBJECTIVE 11 Describe the function of a tee and a cross and give their schematic symbols
SKILL 5 Use a tee to connect two circuit branches together
SKILL 6 Use a cross to connect three circuit branches together

SEGMENT 4 BASIC CYLINDER CIRCUITS... **49**
OBJECTIVE 12 Describe the function of a pneumatic cylinder and give an application
OBJECTIVE 13 Describe the operation of a double-acting pneumatic cylinder and give its schematic symbol
    Activity 2 Basic operation of a double-acting cylinder
OBJECTIVE 14 Describe the function of a 4-way, 3-position pneumatic DCV and give an application
OBJECTIVE 15 Describe the operation of a 4-way, 3-position pneumatic DCV and give its schematic symbol
SKILL 7 Connect and operate a double-acting pneumatic cylinder using a 3-position, manually-operated DCV
SKILL 8 Design a multiple cylinder pneumatic circuit

SEGMENT 1

INTRODUCTION TO PNEUMATICS

OBJECTIVE 1	DEFINE PNEUMATICS AND GIVE AN APPLICATION

All machines require some type of power source and a way of transmitting it to the point of operation. The three methods of transmitting power are mechanical, electrical, and fluid.

Fluid power deals with the transmission and control of energy by means of a pressurized fluid. Although it is common to think of a fluid as simply a liquid, a fluid is actually considered to be either a gas or a liquid. Hence, there are two primary branches of fluid power:

- **Hydraulics -** Which uses a liquid, usually oil
- **Pneumatics -** Which uses a gas, usually air

An example of how pneumatics can be used for energy transmission is shown in figure 1. In this example, a pneumatic system drives a jackhammer to break concrete. An air compressor supplies fluid energy in the form of compressed air through a hose to the jackhammer. Inside the jackhammer, the fluid energy is changed to mechanical energy to drive the bit into the concrete.

Figure 1.   Using Pneumatics to Break Concrete

Pneumatics is an important part of modern industry. Pneumatically-powered machinery will probably be worked with in almost any industrial career. The following are some applications that use pneumatics:

Manufacturing
- Robots
- Conveyor Positioners
- Punch Presses
- Chip Blowing
- Clamping Devices

Transportation
- Truck Brakes
- Vehicle Control Devices

Construction
- Rock Drills
- Sand Blasting
- Power Drills
- Environmental Controls

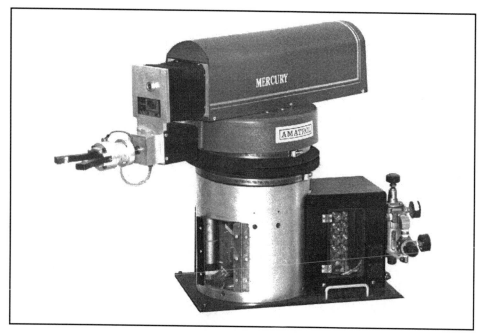

Figure 2. Pneumatic Robot

Pneumatics has many of the same advantages as hydraulic systems: its actuators can be stopped without hurting them, actuator motion can be linear or rotary, and speed is easy to control.

Pneumatics has some other advantages over hydraulics which include:
- **High Speed** - Very high speeds can be obtained with pneumatics.
- **Not Messy** - Pneumatic systems don't leak oil so they are better suited for applications such as textiles or electronics.
- **Low Cost** - Pneumatic system components are lower in cost than hydraulic components because they are designed for operation at much lower pressures.

Pneumatics is not without its disadvantages, however. Pneumatic systems usually don't operate above 150 psi. This means that they are suited only for lower force applications. Also, the compressibility of the gas causes pneumatic actuator motion to be rough, not smooth like hydraulics.

All pneumatic systems consist of five basic components:
- **Power Input Device -** This is the pump that provides pneumatic power to the system. In pneumatics, this pump is called an air compressor. The air compressor draws air from the atmosphere, compresses it and pushes it into the supply line.
- **Control Devices -** Valves control direction, pressure, and flow rate of the pressurized air of the pneumatic system.
- **Power Output Device -** This is where the pneumatic power is converted to mechanical power. These output devices are called actuators. Two types of actuators are motors and cylinders. The motor creates rotary motion as the air flows through it. The cylinder creates straight line motion when air flows into it.
- **Conductors -** To transmit the air, conductors (pipes, tubes, or hoses) are needed. The main line in a pneumatic system is called the supply line, which provides a flow of air to the actuators. The air leaving the actuators is exhausted to the atmosphere.
- **Gas -** This is our power conducting medium. Typically, this is air from the atmosphere but other gases are sometimes used.

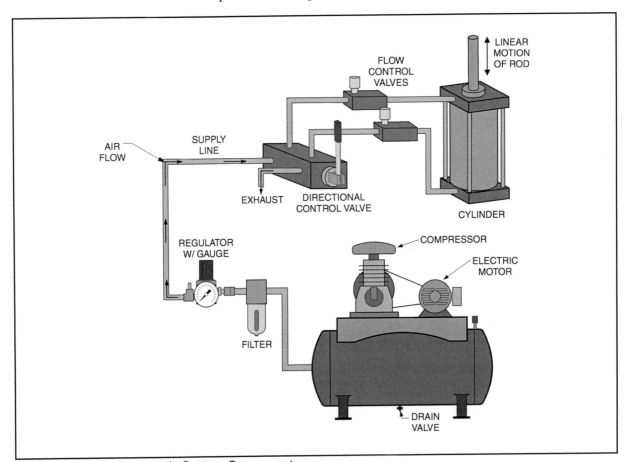

Figure 3.   Basic Pneumatic System Components

Activity 1. Pneumatic Trainer

Procedure Overview

In this activity, you will identify the components of the Amatrol 850 Series pneumatic trainer. This activity will familiarize you with the components used in a pneumatic system.

❑ 1. Position yourself in front of the Amatrol 850 Series pneumatic trainer shown in figure 4.

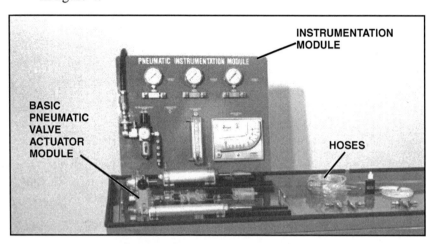

Figure 4.   Amatrol 850 Series Pneumatic Trainer

❑ 2. Locate the **Instrumentation Module**.

This includes pressure gauges and two flow meters to monitor your circuits.

❑ 3. Locate the **Basic Pneumatic Valve Actuator Module**.

This includes several types of valves, two cylinders, and a motor which you will use to build circuits.

❑ 4. Locate the **Air Compressor** used for your classroom.

This unit has a pump, electric motor, air tank, and other components to supply power to the system. This air compressor may be located in another room.

❑ 5. Locate the **Hoses**.

The hoses will be used to connect the components. These are stored behind the instrumentation panel or in a drawer of your bench.

❑ 6. Locate each of the following components on the trainer shown in figure 5.

Each component's name is silkscreened next to it on its mounting panel. Use these labels to identify the location of each component.

COMPONENT	LETTER
PRESSURE GAUGE	
MOTOR	
CYLINDER	
DIRECTIONAL CONTROL VALVE	
PRESSURE REGULATOR VALVE	
FLOW CONTROL VALVE	

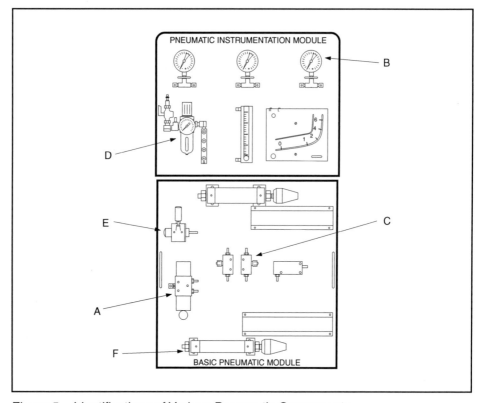

Figure 5.   Identifications of Various Pneumatic Components

An important concept in pneumatics is pressure. Pressure is the intensity of force. It is created when a force from one object acts over an area of another object.

For example, in figure 6, the weight of the box creates a total force of 32 Newtons on the surface on which it is resting. However, the force is actually distributed evenly over the entire area of 4 square meters. This means that a percentage of the total force (32 N) acts on each square meter of the surface. In this case, it would be 8 Newtons for each square meter ($32 \div 4 = 8$). The pressure is said to be 8 Newtons per square meter or 8 N/m^2.

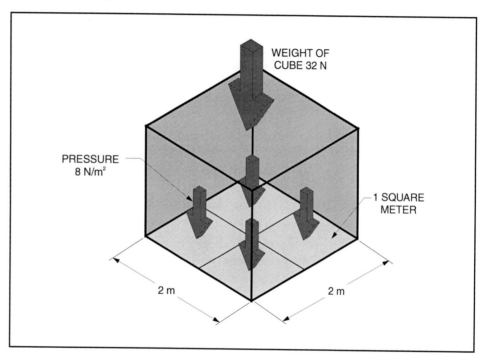

Figure 6.   Pressure is determined by the force and area.

The pressure created by any force can easily be calculated by dividing the total force by the total area as the following formula shows. The most common units in the U.S. Customary system are inches and pounds. This creates the unit of pressure called psi or lbs/in². The most common units in the S.I. system are Newtons and meters. This creates a unit of pressure called a Pascal (Pa). A Pascal is equal to 1 N/m².

FORMULA: PRESSURE/FORCE/AREA RELATIONSHIP

$$Pressure = \frac{Force}{Area}$$

S.I. Units:
  Pressure = *Pascals (Pa), which is equal to 1 N/m²*
  Force = *Newtons (N)*
  Area = *Square Meters (m²)*

U.S. Customary Units:
  Pressure = *psi (lbs/in²)*
  Force = *Pounds (lbs)*
  Area = *Square Inches (in²)*

To further see how pressure and force are different but related, look at figure 7. When the weight is laid on its side, it creates a pressure of 2 N/m² (5 ÷ 2.5 = 2). But when it is laid on its end, the pressure is 5 N/m² (5 ÷ 1 = 5). The same force creates two different pressures by acting over different amounts of area.

This same result occurs in people's shoes. If a woman with a high-heeled shoe steps on you, it hurts much more than if it is a flat-soled shoe. This is because the pressure is higher with the smaller heel.

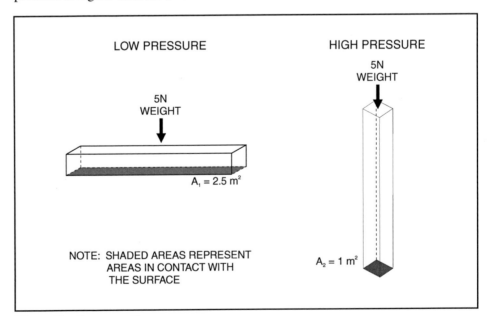

Figure 7. Force vs. Pressure

In addition to mechanical pressure, as shown in figure 7, gas also produces a pressure. This is called fluid pressure or air pressure. A simple way to create air pressure is to place a weight on a container filled with air, as shown in figure 8. This weight pushes down on the air and causes it to be compressed or reduced in volume. The air compresses until its pressure is enough to support the weight.

The air pressure will be the same at every point in the container. A Frenchman named Blaise Pascal discovered this concept in the seventeenth century. It is called Pascal's Law. More about Pascal's Law will be discussed in a later LAP.

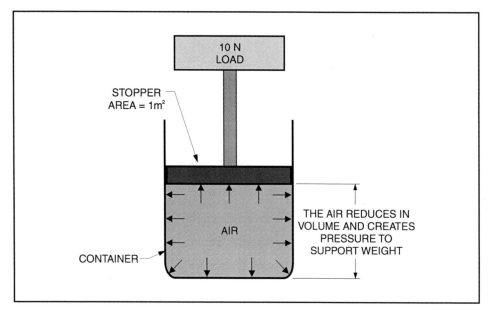

Figure 8.   Pascal's Law

The amount of air pressure created in the container is determined using the P=F/A formula, where the force is the weight and the area is the area of stopper. In figure 8, for example, the pressure is 10 N/m^2 ($10 \div 1.0 = 10$).

The concept shown in figure 8 actually has an application with pneumatic cylinders and air compressors which will be covered later.

Procedure Overview

A pressure gauge indicates the pressure in the pneumatic system. Technicians read pressure gauges in industry to determine if the machine is operating correctly.

In this procedure, you will learn how to read a pressure gauge using the Amatrol pneumatic trainer.

❑ 1. Locate gauge A on the pneumatic trainer's instrumentation panel, as shown in figure 9.

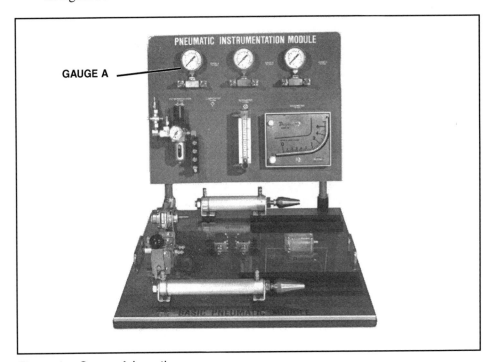

Figure 9.   Gauge A Location

Most pressure gauges have a face plate graduated in either U.S. Customary units (psi) or metric units (Pascals). A pointer rotates around the scaled face plate as the pressure changes to indicate the pressure in the system.

Gauge A actually has two scales to enable it to read both U.S. Customary units and metric units. The outer black scale indicates units of psi. The inner blue scale indicates kilo Pascals (kPa). One kPa is equal to 1000 Pascals. 6.9 kPa is equal to 1 psi.

Each scale is graduated with a series of numbers ranging from 0 to some number. In the case of the Gauge A, the maximum reading possible is 1100 kPa or 160 psi. This maximum reading is commonly called the range of the gauge.

To read a pressure gauge, you only have to look at the number on the blue or black scale to which the pointer points. For example, the pressure reading shown for the gauge in figure 10 is 100 psi or about 690 kPa.

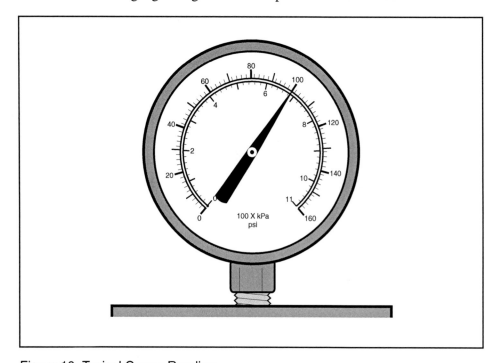

Figure 10. Typical Gauge Reading

NOTE

The gauges on your trainer may show a kPa scale with units of 0 to 11. If so, notice that "100 X kPa" is printed at the bottom of the gauge face. This means that the kPa readings you take from the scale must be multiplied by 100 to get the actual reading. For example, a reading of 7 is really 700 kPa.

If the pointer points to a position between two numbers, as shown in Gauge 1 of figure 11, you read the gauge to the closest graduation.

For example, in Gauge 1 of figure 11, the pointer is positioned between 200 and 400 kPa. Notice that there are 10 graduations between 200 and 400. This means the value of each graduation is 20 kPa. Since the pointer is pointing to the first graduation, the pressure being indicated is 220 kPa.

❑ 2. Practice your ability to read a pressure gauge by determining the readings shown for each gauge in figure 11.

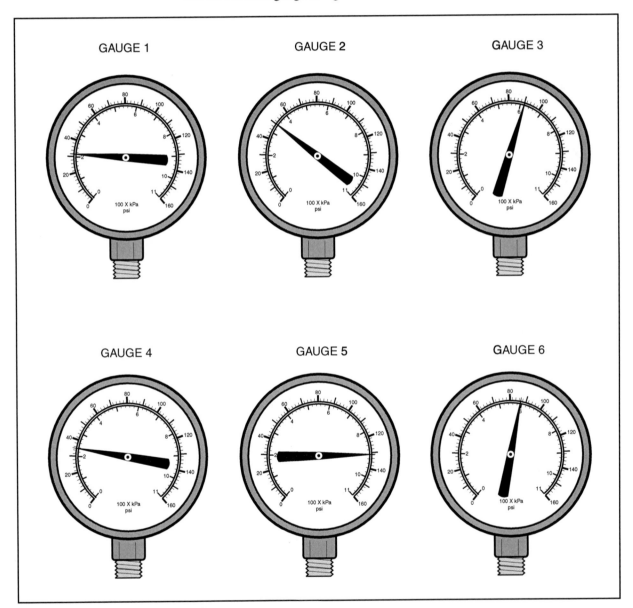

Figure 11.   Various Gauge Readings

GAUGE	PRESSURE (psi/kPa)
1	/
2	/
3	/
4	/
5	/
6	/

The answers for these are: Gauge 1 =32 psi / 220 kPa, Gauge 2 =50 psi / 340 kPa, Gauge 3 =90 psi / 620 kPa, Gauge 4 =36 psi / 240 kPa, Gauge 5 =132 psi / 900 kPa, Gauge 6 =86 psi / 600 kPa

❑ 3. Now locate the system pressure gauge, Gauge S, on the pressure regulator, as shown in figure 12. The pointer on this gauge should be indicating 0.

Notice that the units of MPa is used instead of the kPa unit for one of the scales. An MPa is equal to 1000 kPa. To convert this scale to kPa, just move the decimal three places to the right. For example, 0.2 MPa is equal to 200 kPa.

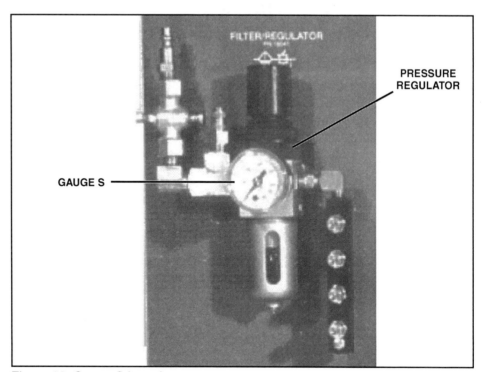

Figure 12. Gauge S Location

❑ 4. Determine the following about Gauge S.

A. Full Scale Reading _____ psi _____kPa

B. Major Graduation Unit _____ psi _____kPa

C. Minor Graduation Unit _____ psi _____kPa

You should find that the full scale (FS) reading is 160 psi/1100 kPa, major unit 20 psi/100 kPa, and minor unit 2 psi/20 kPa.

It is important to know that pressure gauges are not perfectly accurate. All gauges have an error. Manufacturers state the error of the gauge in their catalog data sheet. It is stated as a percent of the FS reading. For example, if a 1000-psi gauge has an error of ±5% FS (full scale), the actual pressure could be different from the reading by 50 psi (0.05 x 1000). A good pressure gauge should have a FS reading error of 0.5% or 1%.

A point you should also keep in mind is that the amount of error does not depend on the actual pressure reading. For example, if the pressure gauge's FS is 1000 psi and its error is ±5% of FS (i.e. 50 psi in this case), the error is ±50 psi whether the actual reading is 200 psi or 1000 psi. This means that your gauge is not very accurate if the pressure is at the bottom of its range.

Before covering more complex pneumatic circuits, we must first look at the way these components are represented in a diagram. A pneumatic diagram shows how the components in a circuit are connected so that we can understand what the circuit does and how it works.

In some cases, pneumatic diagrams can be shown as pictorials, where actual pictures are used. While pictorials allow us to easily see what the devices look like, they are very time consuming to draw and actually harder to use. To solve this problem, schematic diagrams are used.

A schematic diagram is a form of visual shorthand where standard symbols represent each component. A schematic diagram shows all the components in a circuit and their interconnections. Except when noted, a schematic diagram shows all the components in their de-energized state.

An example of a typical pneumatic schematic that uses standard symbols is shown in figure 13.

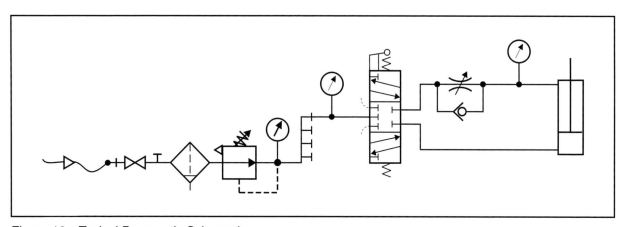

Figure 13. Typical Pneumatic Schematic

Notice the hollow (open) triangle on the far left side of figure 13. This symbol is commonly used in pneumatics to show flow direction as well as a shortcut for indicating an air supply. When used to indicate air supply, all components and lines used up to that point to provide the supply need not be shown.

As each new pneumatic component is introduced, the symbol for each device will be shown. Most symbols use an elementary form to identify the general function of the component. These forms are circles, squares, rectangles, triangles, arcs, arrows, and lines, as shown in figure 14. These basic symbol forms are combined together to form symbols of various components.

SYMBOL	SYMBOL
◯ ROTATING DEVICE	↗ VARIABLE
☐ VALVE	≍ RESTRICTION
◇ CONDITIONING DEVICE	+ LINES CONNECTED
▭ CYLINDER	⋀⋀ SPRING
⬭ STORAGE	⟶✕ BLOCKED
—— CONDUCTOR	⊣ BLOCKED LINE
⟶▷ FLOW DIRECTION	

Figure 14. Elementary Forms of Symbols

Three standards that are most often referenced for symbols are those developed by the National Fluid Power Association (NFPA), American National Standards Institute (ANSI), and the International Organization for Standardization (ISO). The organization uses ISO instead of IOS because, although not a correct acronym, it is easier to remember. ISO is from the Greek word "isos", meaning equal.

The United States uses NFPA and ANSI standards. The rest of the world, as well as the U.S., uses the ISO standard.

NOTE

As you progress through the rest of this LAP, you will learn the symbol for each component and how to read schematics that contain them.

1. _____ is the fluid most used in pneumatics to transmit power.

2. The power output device of a pneumatic system is known as the _____.

3. Pressure is a measure of _____ intensity.

4. The maximum pressure indication on a pressure gauge is called the _____ of the gauge.

5. A(n) _____ diagram shows how the components in a circuit are connected.

SEGMENT 2

PNEUMATIC POWER

OBJECTIVE 5   **EXPLAIN SIX PNEUMATIC SAFETY RULES**

Although most pneumatic power systems operate at low pressures of 100 psi/690 kPa or less, special care must still be taken to prevent injury or damage to equipment. Apply the following safety rules when working with or around pneumatic power systems.

- **Do not point compressed air at eyes, ears, mouth, nose, or skin.** This includes blocking a compressed air line or fitting with fingers or hands. The air can inject itself into the skin.
- **Properly secure a hose or device that contains compressed air.** Fittings can blow out if they are not secure. Mechanically test or pull connections before pressurizing. Tie or hold down open, loose lines to avoid whipping when connecting into live pressure lines. Always turn off the air pressure before connecting equipment and gradually turn up the pressure where possible while observing for loose lines.
- **Use proper pressures when cleaning with air.** Do not use air lines at full pressure to blow or clean parts. Reduce to 30 psi or below.
- **Use safety glasses.** Safety glasses with side shields should be used when cleaning or working with compressed air that can be released, although they are not absolute protection.
- **Use strong enough containers to safely hold compressed air.** Use only approved pressure-rated containers for compressed air storage. Replace old and worn pressure lines.
- **Avoid continuous noise exposure.** The noise caused by the exhaust of a pneumatic component can be damaging to the ears at certain levels or at least annoying.

OBJECTIVE 6 — DESCRIBE THE FUNCTION OF A PRESSURE REGULATOR VALVE AND GIVE AN APPLICATION

The air pressures needed for applications in different areas of the plant are often less than the pressure available from the main compressed air supply. To reduce the pressure in these areas, a pressure regulator valve is used.

The pressure regulator valve controls the pressure downstream from its outlet. It is designed to maintain a constant downstream pressure.

You will find that regulators are located at almost every station in a manufacturing plant to allow each station to operate at the exact pressure needed for each application.

Figure 15. A Standard Industrial Regulator

Unlike hydraulic systems, where the pump produces flow not pressure, the air compressor does just the opposite. It produces pressure not flow. Flow only occurs where there is a difference in pressure between two points in the system.

The pressure regulator consists of a body, poppet, springs, piston, and a means of adjustment, as shown in figure 16.

The poppet opens and closes to provide the correct pressure downstream (at the outlet) by restricting the air flow. There are two springs: one for the adjustment and the other to make the poppet close. The adjustment knob changes the compression on the spring which controls the level of downstream pressure. The piston is attached to one end of the poppet to provide a surface for the spring to push on.

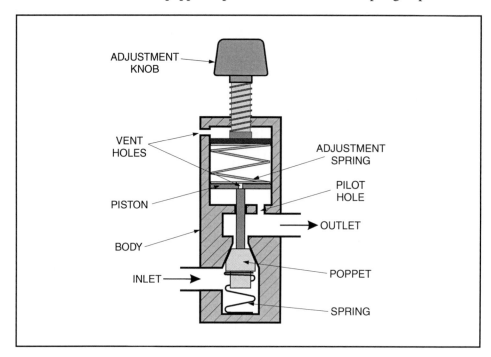

Figure 16. Typical Pressure Regulator

The schematic symbol for a pressure regulator is shown in figure 17. The symbol shows a valve that is normally open because the flow line through the valve connects the inlet and outlet. The dashed line represents a pilot line inside the valve body which senses downstream pressure. The spring shows that it opposes the downstream pressure. The arrow through the spring indicates that the pressure setting is adjustable. Finally, the triangle on the inlet side shows that this regulator is self-bleeding, a feature that will be explained in Skill 2.

Also, notice that a pressure gauge is shown with the regulator. Many regulators are made with a port for attaching a pressure gauge directly to them.

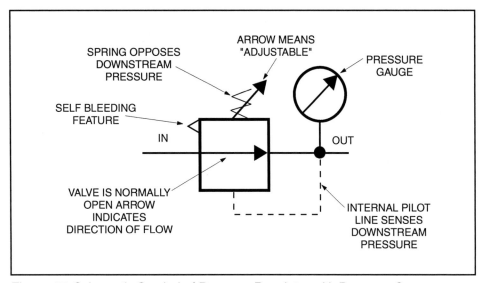

Figure 17. Schematic Symbol of Pressure Regulator with Pressure Gauge

As shown in figure 18, the regulator with pressure gauge is used to reduce the supply pressure to the control and power circuit of the machine. Normally it is located in the circuit between a filter and the control valves.

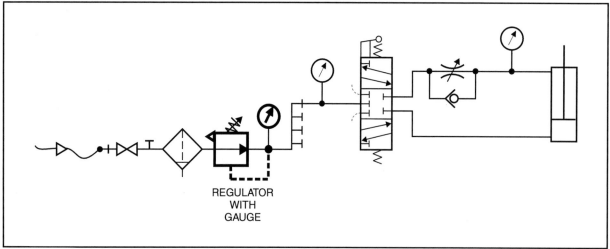

REGULATOR
WITH
GAUGE

Figure 18. Location of the Regulator with Gauge in a Pneumatic Circuit

SKILL 2	CONNECT AND ADJUST A PRESSURE REGULATOR

Procedure Overview

Adjusting the outlet pressure of a pressure regulator is a common task in industry. In this procedure, you will adjust the regulator to several different settings.

❑ 1. Position yourself in front of the Amatrol 85-BP Basic Pneumatic trainer.

❑ 2. Locate the regulator on the instrumentation module. You will find it mounted at the lower left corner, as shown in figure 19.

This is a pressure regulator combination unit which includes an air filter and a pressure gauge. This pressure gauge measures downstream pressure.

In this circuit, the inlet is blocked from the supply by a shutoff valve. The outlet is connected to a 4-ported supply manifold. The schematic of this circuit is shown in figure 20.

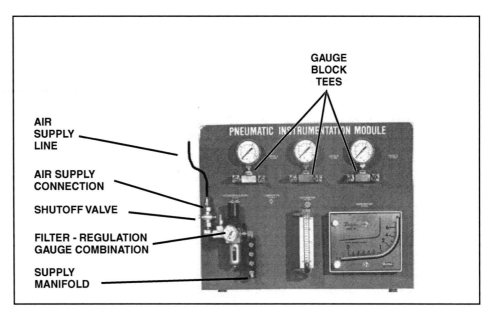

Figure 19. The Amatrol 850 Pneumatic Filter-Regulator and Supply Components

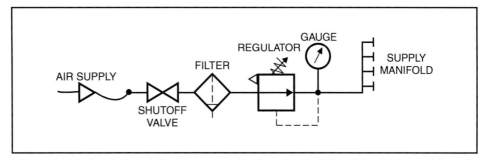

Figure 20. Schematic of the Amatrol 850 Pneumatic Filter-Regulator and Supply Components

❑ 3. Perform the following substeps to set up the regulator for adjusting.

    A. Close the shutoff valve if not already closed. When closed, the shutoff valve handle will be perpendicular to the plumbing, as shown in figure 21.

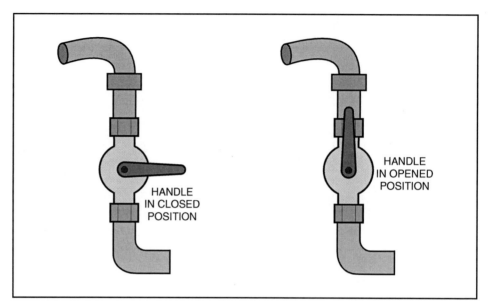

Figure 21. Amatrol 850 Shutoff Valve

    B. Adjust the regulator to its minimum pressure setting by pulling up on its knob to unlock it and then screwing the knob counterclockwise (CCW) fully.

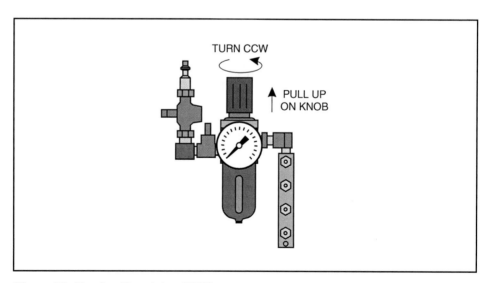

Figure 22. Turning Regulator CCW

C. If not already attached, have your instructor connect the compressed air supply source to the supply connection, as shown in figure 23.

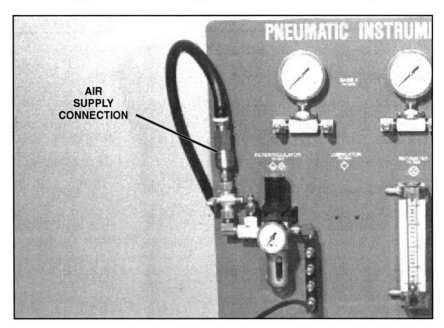

Figure 23. Air Supply Connection

D. Open the shutoff valve by turning the shutoff valve handle to a position parallel with the plumbing, as shown in figure 21.

This will allow the air from the supply line to flow to the inlet of the regulator, as shown in figure 24. You should observe that the regulator's gauge still shows 0 psi/0 kPa because the regulator is set at its minimum pressure and is, therefore, blocking pressure flow to the outlet.

With the adjustment knob turned fully out (CCW), there is no tension (compression) on the adjustment spring. The poppet spring keeps the poppet seated, blocking air flow from the inlet. With no air flow to the outlet, no air pressure is seen at the downstream pressure gauge, which is the regulator gauge.

NOTE

The upstream pressure gauge in figures 24 through 26 is shown for explanation purposes. It is not hooked up on your trainer at this time.

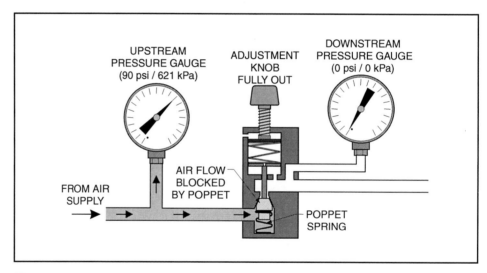

Figure 24. Pressure Regulator Adjusted to 0 psi / 0 kPa - Knob Fully Out

❑ 4. Adjust the downstream pressure of the pressure regulator to 30 psi/ 207 kPa by pulling up on the knob to unlock it and then screwing the knob clockwise (CW).

When the adjustment knob is turned CW, the adjustment spring compresses against the top of the piston. The piston forces the poppet to open, allowing air to flow from the inlet to the outlet, as shown in figure 25.

As pressure builds at the outlet, it is also felt on the bottom of the piston because of the pilot hole. When the outlet air pressure on the piston overcomes the adjustment spring force, the poppet is allowed to move to close off flow. Outlet pressure continues to build until the poppet closes completely, blocking air flow. The poppet closes completely when the downstream pressure gauge reads 30 psi/207 kPa.

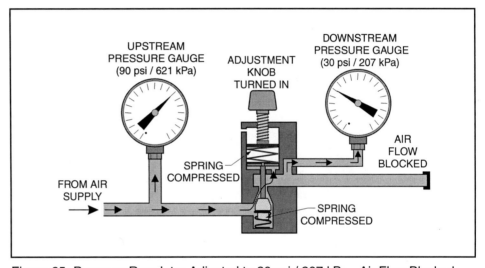

Figure 25. Pressure Regulator Adjusted to 30 psi / 207 kPa - Air Flow Blocked

The reason the poppet closes completely in this case is because the outlet is blocked. If a manifold port is open, the regulator can still maintain a constant downstream pressure. The basic operation is still the same except that the regulator poppet is partially open to allow air to flow.

To understand how this works, here's what happens:

When air is allowed to flow through the downstream line, the pressure on the outlet side of the regulator drops slightly. Since there is now less air pressure on the piston, the adjustment spring pushes it down, opening the poppet. This allows air to flow from the inlet side. The poppet will continue to open wider to allow the air flow to increase until the pressure at the outlet reaches the regulator's pressure setting. At this point, the poppet is open part way. As air flows through the line, the poppet will adjust the amount of its opening to provide a balance between air pressure and air flow.

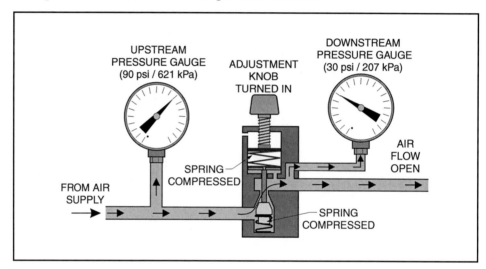

Figure 26. Pressure Regulator at 30 psi / 207 kPa - With Air Flow

❑ 5. Repeat step 4 for pressures of 40 psi / 276 kPa and 60 psi / 414 kPa to test your ability to adjust the pressure setting of the regulator.

❑ 6. Now turn the regulator knob CW until the pressure no longer rises. Record this pressure.

This is the maximum pressure of your supply. At this setting, the regulator is fully opened.

Supply Pressure_____ (psi/kPa)

❑ 7. Perform the following substeps to adjust the regulator back to 30 psi/207 kPa:

A. Lift the knob and screw it CCW until the pressure reads below 25 psi/173 kPa. During this operation, you will hear the air vent itself as the regulator gauge drops. This is the "self-bleed" feature in this regulator.

Most regulators are of the self-bleed type. This means they automatically drop the outlet pressure when the pressure adjustment is decreased, as shown in figure 27.

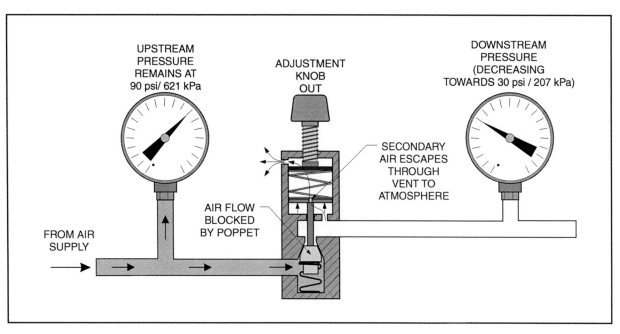

Figure 27. Regulator Relieving

B. Now screw the knob CW to the 30 psi/207 kPa setting.

This technique of adjusting the pressure below the setting and then increasing it to the desired setting should always be used.

❑ 8. Close the shutoff valve.

❑ 9. Decrease the regulator setting to minimum by lifting the knob and screwing it fully CCW.

You should observe the regulator gauge reads 0 psi/0 kPa.

The compressed air used in pneumatics comes from the atmosphere. That means the air supply contains dust, pollution, and other small particles which are too small to see.

Components such as cylinders and valves have close fitting parts which must slide back and forth. Dirt will keep these parts from working smoothly.

An air filter is a device designed to clean the air before it enters the pneumatic system. It will also remove water droplets from the air supply, but not water vapor. All pneumatic systems should be installed with one or more air filters.

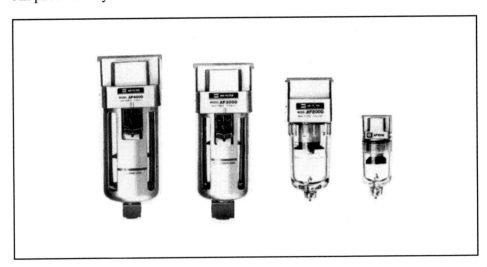

Figure 28. Pneumatic Filters

The construction of an air filter and its schematic symbol are shown in figure 29.

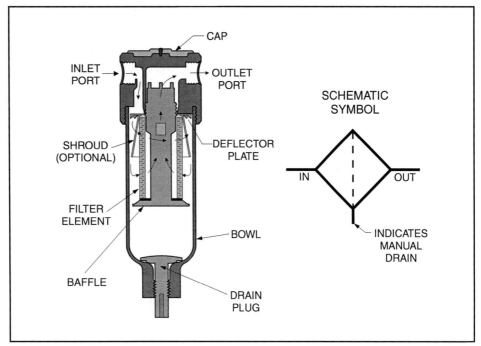

Figure 29. Construction of a Typical Air Filter and its Schematic Symbol

The only moving item in an air filter is the air itself. The air coming into the filter hits a deflector. The deflector makes the air spin around the inside of the filter bowl. This spinning action throws the heavier particles against the sides of the bowl where they drop past the baffle to the bottom.

The air then swirls into the filter element. The smaller particles are trapped in the filter element and the clean air passes through the outlet connection.

Water that has collected in the filter bowl must be drained before the level reaches the bottom of the baffle.

On the Amatrol 850 Series pneumatic trainer, the filter is located ahead of and beneath the regulator with gauge. It is common practice to install a filter just ahead of the regulator to protect the regulator and other downstream precision operating components from harmful dirt and water particles.

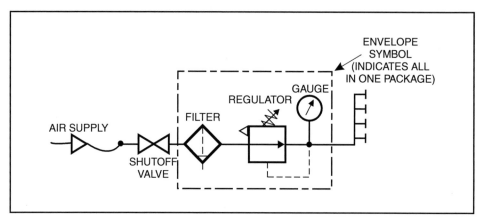

Figure 30. Schematic Symbol of the Filter-Regulator on the Amatrol 850 Series Pneumatic Trainer

Procedure Overview

Proper maintenance of the filter requires that you drain water that collects in the filter. In this procedure, you will operate the drain on the filter-regulator.

CAUTION

This procedure will be conducted with pressure at the filter-regulator. Be careful not to spray the excess water.

❑ 1. Close the shutoff valve.

❑ 2. Locate the drain at the base of the filter-regulator's bowl. On this regulator it looks just like a tire valve.

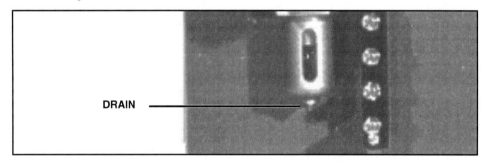

DRAIN

Figure 31. Filter Drain

❑ 3. While holding a towel or an absorbent rag beneath the bowl, use a screwdriver or rod to press in easy on the drain valve. If there is water in the filter bowl, it will be blown into your towel.

❑ 4. Release the drain valve by removing pressure on the drain valve. The spring of the drain valve will close it.

1. The device used to clean air is called a(n) _____.

2. A pressure regulator is used to _____ downstream pressure.

3. To decrease regulated pressure, turn the regulator adjustment knob _____.

4. A pressure regulator's _____ opens and closes to provide the correct pressure downstream by restricting the air flow.

5. The outlet pressure of a regulator automatically drops off as pressure is decreased if it has a(n) _____ _____ feature.

6. The _____ of the filter makes the air spin to throw heavier particles against the sides of the bowl.

7. Air flow out of an opened and unrestricted hose end will cause the hose to _____.

SEGMENT 3

CIRCUIT CONNECTIONS

OBJECTIVE 10	DESCRIBE THE FUNCTION OF A PNEUMATIC QUICK-CONNECT FITTING AND GIVE ITS SCHEMATIC SYMBOL

Pneumatic systems often use flexible hoses. Sometimes these hoses use quick-connect fittings to connect them to the components. As its name implies, a quick-connect fitting allows fast and easy assembly and disassembly of circuits.

Quick-connect fittings consist of a male-end fitting and a female-end fitting, as shown in figure 32. These fittings snap together without special tools.

Industry uses quick-connect fittings where there is a frequent need to disconnect a hose. An air supply hose for a portable air compressor is an example.

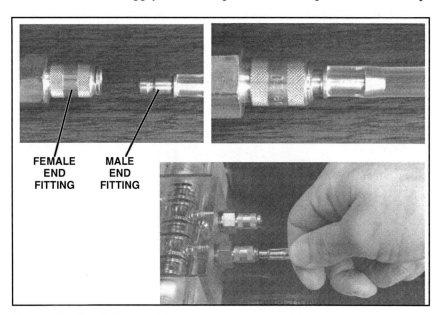

Figure 32. Quick-Connect Fittings

The schematic symbol for a quick-connect fitting is shown in figure 33. This symbol shows two types of fittings connected to each other. One fitting has a check valve and the other does not. The check valve closes when the fittings are disconnected so pressurized air does not escape. The other fitting is open to atmosphere when it is disconnected.

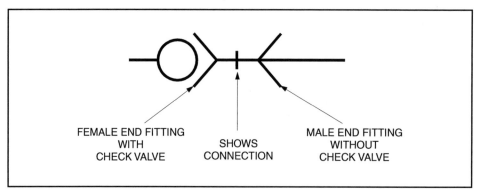

FEMALE END FITTING
WITH
CHECK VALVE

SHOWS
CONNECTION

MALE END FITTING
WITHOUT
CHECK VALVE

Figure 33. Schematic Symbol for Pneumatic Quick-Connect Fittings

SKILL 4	CONNECT A PNEUMATIC HOSE THAT USES QUICK-CONNECT FITTINGS

Procedure Overview

In this procedure, you will connect a pressure gauge to the outlet side of a regulator using a tube equipped with quick-connect fittings. You will then put pressure on the system to test your connection.

❏ 1. Set up the circuit shown in figure 34 by connecting a tube with quick-connect fittings from the supply manifold to gauge C. Pull on each end of the tube after you connect it. If it holds, you've made a good connection.

In order to connect a tube to a pneumatic component, grasp the tube and push its plug into the proper socket connection on the component until the socket clicks. To check the firmness of the connection, pull on the tube. If you do not completely engage the quick-connects, the tube's male plug will come out. It also means that the valve in the female socket was not opened to pass air. It is necessary to completely engage the plug and socket to make a good connection.

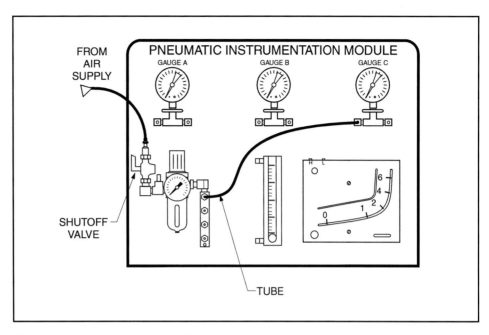

FROM AIR SUPPLY

PNEUMATIC INSTRUMENTATION MODULE

GAUGE A GAUGE B GAUGE C

SHUTOFF VALVE

TUBE

Figure 34. Using A Tube with Quick-Connects

❏ 2. If not already connected, connect the compressed air supply to the male quick-connect on the instrumentation module and open the shutoff valve.

❏ 3. Lift and turn the regulator knob CW until the pressure at the regulator gauge reads 20 psi/138 kPa.

Record Gauge C pressure.

Gauge C _____ (psi/kPa)

It should be close to the reading of the regulator gauge. If it is, you have correctly connected the tube and the gauges are working correctly.

❏ 4. Increase the pressure at the regulator to 60 psi/414 kPa.

Record Gauge C pressure.

Gauge C _____ (psi/kPa)

Again, both gauges should closely agree.

❏ 5. Close the shutoff valve.

❏ 6. Decrease the pressure at the regulator to minimum.

❏ 7. Disconnect the tube between the supply manifold and Gauge C by pulling on the collar of the female socket. The tube end with its male plug will eject with little or no help.

The valve in the body of the female socket prevents pressurized air from escaping. The male plug has no valve and air is free to pass. Valves are not necessary in pneumatic tube male plug connectors since the air itself should be exhausted, along with any water accumulation from condensation.

DESCRIBE THE FUNCTION OF A TEE AND A CROSS AND GIVE THEIR SCHEMATIC SYMBOLS

Some pneumatic circuits have more than one branch circuit. To connect two branch circuits to a single supply line, a fitting called a tee is used. A tee is actually shaped like a "T."

The loose components supplied with the 850 Series pneumatic system include two fitting tees. They are both equipped with female quick-connect fittings, as shown in figure 35. These fittings will allow you to quickly connect tubes with plugs to these components.

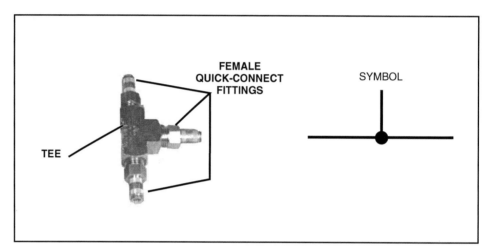

Figure 35. Tee Equipped with Quick-Connect Fittings and Schematic

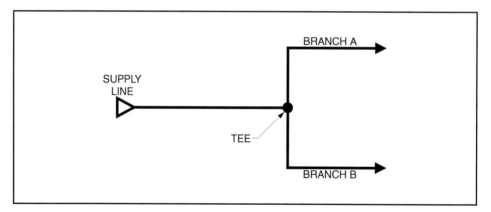

Figure 36. Tee Connection to Two Branch Circuits

Another fitting similar to a tee is a cross. A cross is shaped like a plus sign and provides connections to three branch circuits.

The 850 Series pneumatic system includes one cross which has female quick-connect fittings on all sides, as shown in figure 37.

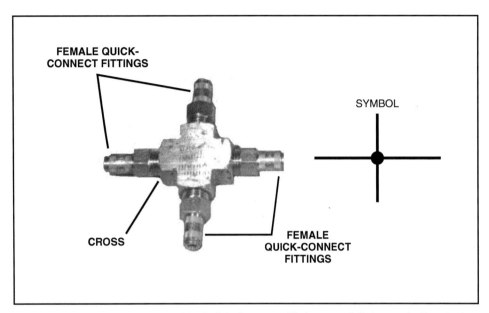

Figure 37. Cross Equipped with Quick-Connect Fittings and Schematic Symbol

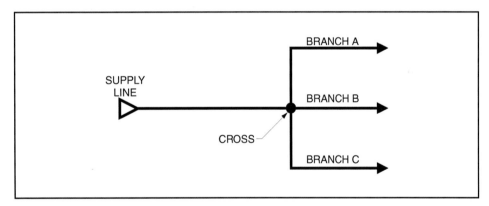

Figure 38. Cross Connection to the Branch Circuit

Procedure Overview

In this procedure, you will connect two pressure gauges to the same supply line using tee fittings. This procedure will help you better understand how tees can be used in a circuit.

□ 1. Set up the circuit shown in the pictorial drawing of figure 39 and schematic drawing of figure 40.

In this circuit, two gauges are connected to the supply manifold by a separate fitting tee.

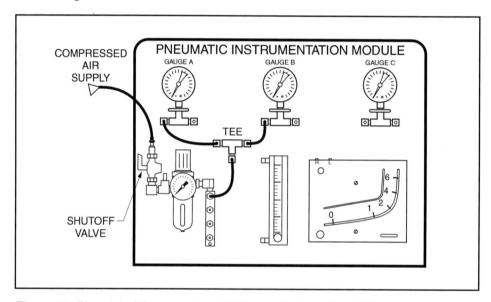

Figure 39. Pictorial of Gauges A and B Connected by a Tee Fitting

Notice in figure 40 that the filter and regulator are drawn separately. This is the standard way to draw the filter and regulator even though they are built into the same body.

The hollow triangle, shown in figure 40, always points in the direction of air flow.

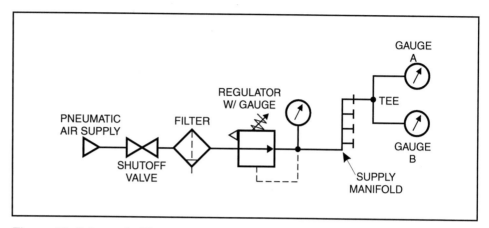

Figure 40. Schematic Diagram

❑ 2. Connect the compressed air supply to the male quick-connect on the instrumentation module and open the shutoff valve.

❑ 3. Turn the regulator adjustment knob CW until the pressure at the regulator reads 20 psi/138 kPa.

❑ 4. Record the pressures indicated at Gauges A and B.

Gauge A _____ (psi/kPa)

Gauge B _____ (psi/kPa)

Both gauges should be close to the reading at the regulator gauge. If they are, you have correctly connected the tee fitting.

❑ 5. Turn the regulator adjustment knob CW until the pressure at the regulator gauge reads 60 psi/414 kPa.

❑ 6. Record the pressures indicated at Gauges A and B.

Gauge A _____ (psi/kPa)

Gauge B _____ (psi/kPa)

Again, both gauges should closely agree.

❑ 7. Close the shutoff valve.

❑ 8. Turn the regulator adjustment CCW fully to reduce the pressure to a minimum.

❑ 9. Now set up the circuit shown in figure 41.

In this circuit, a gauge block tee is used to connect Gauges A and B to the supply manifold. This is the same circuit shown in figure 39.

These gauge block tees do the same thing as the loose fitting tee you used. They are machined from blocks of aluminum. Tees are often directly connected to pressure gauges like you see here because they allow easy connection of a pressure gauge to monitor the pressure in a line.

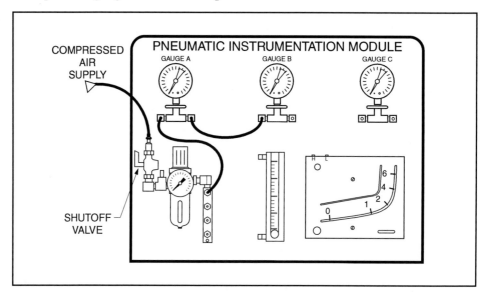

Figure 41. Pictorial of Gauges A and B Connected to the Supply Line Using Gauge Block A Tee

❑10. Open the shutoff valve.

❑11. Turn the regulator adjustment knob CW until the pressure at the regulator gauge is 20 psi/138 kPa.

Record the pressures indicated at Gauges A and B.

Gauge A _____ (psi/kPa)

Gauge B _____ (psi/kPa)

Both gauges should be close to the reading of the regulator. If they are, you have correctly connected the gauge block tee.

❑12. Turn the regulator adjustment knob CW until the pressure at the regulator gauge reads 60 psi/414 kPa.

❑13. Record the pressures indicated at Gauges A and B.

Gauge A _____ (psi/kPa)

Gauge B _____ (psi/kPa)

Again, all gauges should closely agree.

❑14. Turn the regulator adjustment CCW fully to reduce the pressure to a minimum.

❑15. Close the shutoff valve.

❑16. Now change the circuit to the one shown in figure 42.

In this circuit, the gauge block A tee is connected to the other side of the gauge block B tee. This is again the same circuit as shown in figure 39. The schematic shown in figure 40 could represent any one of the physical connections shown in figures 39, 41, and 42.

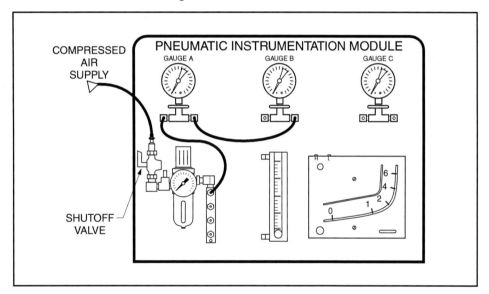

Figure 42. Pictorial of Gauge Block A Tee Connected to the Other Side of Gauge Block B Tee

❑17. Open the shutoff valve.

❑18. Turn the regulator pressure adjustment knob CW until the pressure at the regulator reads 20 psi/138 kPa.

❑19. Record the pressures indicated at Gauges A and B.

Gauge A _____ (psi/kPa)

Gauge B _____ (psi/kPa)

Both gauges should be close to the reading at the regulator gauge because either side of the tee block connects to the gauge.

❑20. Turn the regulator adjustment knob CW until the pressure at the regulator gauge reads 60 psi/414 kPa.

❑21. Record the pressures indicated at Gauges A and B.

Gauge A _____ (psi/kPa)

Gauge B _____ (psi/kPa)

Again, both gauges should closely agree.

❑22. Turn the regulator adjustment CCW fully to reduce the pressure to a minimum.

❑23. Close the shutoff valve.

SKILL 6	USE A CROSS TO CONNECT THREE CIRCUIT BRANCHES TOGETHER

Procedure Overview

In this procedure, you will connect three pressure gauges to the same supply line to demonstrate the operation of a cross.

❑ 1. Set up the circuit shown in figure 43.

In this circuit, the cross connects Gauges A, B, and C to the supply manifold.

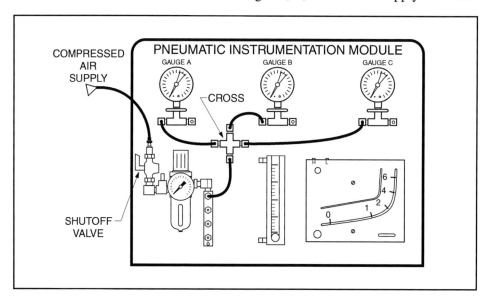

Figure 43. Pictorial of Gauges A, B and C Connected with a Cross

❑ 2. Connect the compressed air supply to the male quick-connect on the instrumentation module and open the shutoff valve. This connects the air supply to the regulator.

❑ 3. Turn the regulator adjustment knob CW until the pressure at the regulator gauge reads 20 psi/138 kPa.

❏ 4. Record the pressures indicated at Gauges A, B, and C.

Gauge A _____ (psi/kPa)

Gauge B _____ (psi/kPa)

Gauge C _____ (psi/kPa)

All three gauges should be close to the reading of the regulator gauge. If they are, you have correctly connected the cross in the circuit.

❏ 5. Turn the regulator adjustment knob CW until the pressure at the regulator gauge reads 60 psi/414 kPa.

❏ 6. Record the pressures indicated at Gauges A, B, and C.

Gauge A _____ (psi/kPa)

Gauge B _____ (psi/kPa)

Gauge C _____ (psi/kPa)

Again, all gauges should closely agree.

❏ 7. Close the shutoff valve.

❏ 8. Turn the regulator adjustment CCW fully to reduce the pressure to a minimum.

1. _____ fittings allow fast and easy assembly and disassembly of circuits.

2. A fitting used to connect three branch circuits to a supply is called a(n) _____.

3. A(n) _____ allows you to connect two branches together.

4. The device that keeps the air from escaping from the quick-connect fitting is called a(n) _____ valve.

5. Always _____ on the tube after making a connection to ensure that it is firmly connected.

SEGMENT 4

BASIC CYLINDER CIRCUITS

OBJECTIVE 12 | **DESCRIBE THE FUNCTION OF A PNEUMATIC CYLINDER AND GIVE AN APPLICATION**

 A pneumatic cylinder is an actuator that converts air power into mechanical power in the form of straight-line motion. A typical cylinder is shown in figure 44.

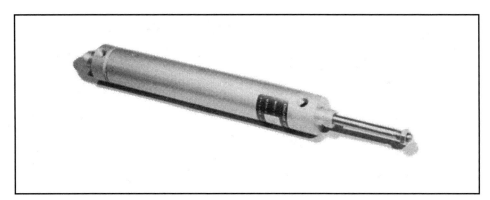

Figure 44. A Typical Pneumatic Cylinder

Applications commonly use pneumatic cylinders for high speed and straight-line motion. One example is a punch press like the one shown in figure 45.

Figure 45. Punch Press

A pneumatic cylinder consists of a piston/rod assembly that can move inside a barrel-shaped body. The most common type of cylinder is a double-acting cylinder like the one shown in figure 46. This type has two ports through which air can enter. When air flows into the cap end, the cylinder rod extends. The cylinder rod retracts when air flows into the rod end. This operation will be explained in more detail in the following activity.

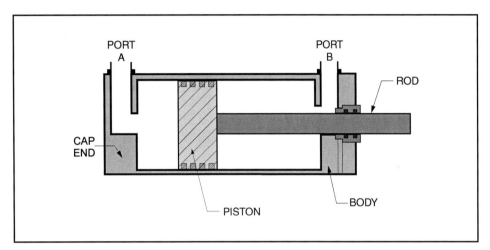

Figure 46. Basic Parts of a Cylinder

The schematic symbol for a double-acting cylinder is shown in figure 47.

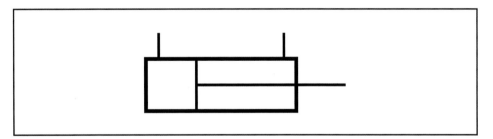

Figure 47. Schematic Symbol of Double-Acting Cylinder

Activity 2. Basic Operation of a Double-Acting Cylinder

Procedure Overview

In this procedure, you will connect and operate a cylinder by switching two hoses between the ports of the cylinder. This will demonstrate the basic operation of the cylinder.

❏ 1. Before you connect your cylinder circuit, perform the following substeps.

    A. Close the shutoff valve if not already closed.

    B. Adjust the pressure regulator to minimum by pulling up on the knob to unlock it and then screwing the knob counterclockwise (CCW) fully.

    C. If not already attached, connect the compressed air supply source to the supply connection located on the pneumatic instrumentation module.

❏ 2. Set up the pneumatic circuit shown in figure 48.

In this circuit, the regulated supply is connected directly to the cap end of the cylinder. An air line must be connected to the rod end to allow air to flow freely out of the cylinder.

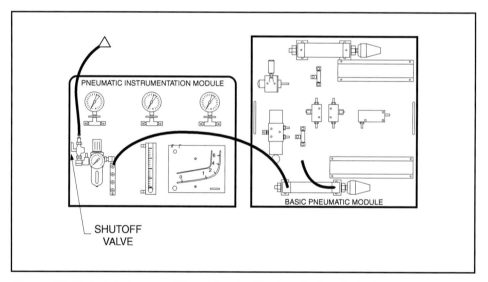

Figure 48. Pictorial of a Circuit to Extend a Double-Acting Cylinder

❑ 3. Open the shutoff valve.

This will connect the air supply to the regulator. You are now ready to extend the cylinder.

❑ 4. Lift the knob of the regulator and turn it slowly CW until the cylinder extends.

You should observe that the cylinder extends at a low pressure because there is no load on the cylinder.

To understand how the cylinder is able to extend, remember that pressure acts on all surfaces in a container with equal force. However, with a cylinder, one wall of the container, the piston, is able to move. When air from the supply enters the cylinder port from the cap end, the air presses against the inside surfaces of the cylinder. This causes the piston to move and extend the rod, as shown in figure 49. As the piston moves, it forces the air on the other side to be pushed out of the rod-end port. This air is exhausted to the atmosphere.

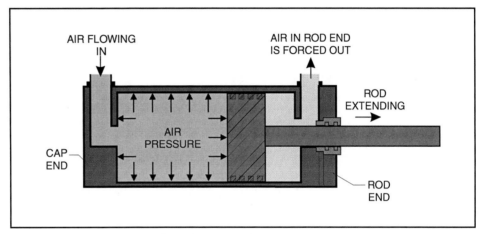

Figure 49. Double-Acting Cylinder Being Extended

At this point, you may be wondering why the air doesn't leak out of the cylinder around the rod. This is because there is a flexible seal called a rod seal that is placed around the rod, as shown in figure 50.

To hold this seal in place, a rod bushing is needed. This bushing also acts as a bearing to support the rod as it extends.

In addition to the rod seal, there is also one or more piston seals. The piston seals keep air from leaking around the piston so pressure can build up to move the load.

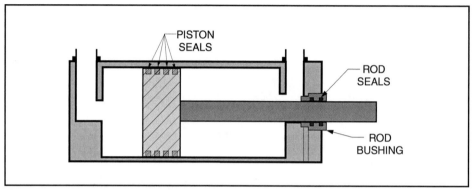

Figure 50. Seals of a Double-Acting Cylinder

❑ 5. Close the shutoff valve.

❑ 6. Reduce the regulator setting back to minimum by turning the knob fully CCW.

❑ 7. Switch the two hoses at the cylinder so that the supply line is connected to the rod end of the cylinder, as shown in figure 51.

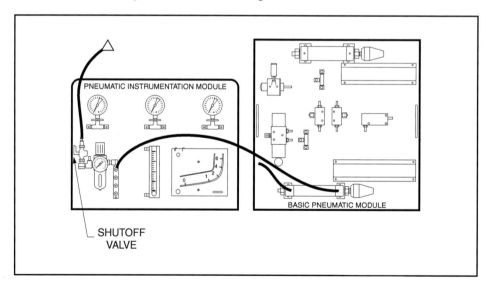

Figure 51. Pictorial of a Circuit to Retract a Double-Acting Cylinder

❑ 8. Open the shut-off valve.

❑ 9. Lift the knob of the regulator and turn it slowly CW until the cylinder retracts.

You should observe that the cylinder retracts at a low pressure.

The cylinder retracted because the air from the supply flowed to the cylinder through the rod-end port, as shown in figure 52. This causes the piston to move in the other direction and retract the rod. When this happens, the piston forces the air in the cap end, out of the cylinder, and back to the atmosphere.

When the piston reaches the end of travel (fully extended or retracted), the air flow in the cylinder stops.

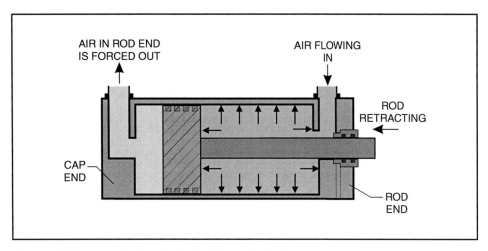

Figure 52. Double-Acting Cylinder Being Retracted

❑10. Close the shutoff valve.

❑11. Reduce the regulator setting back to minimum by turning the knob fully CCW.

❑12. Disconnect the hoses and store them.

To change the direction of the double-acting cylinder without moving hoses, as in the previous skill, a switch is needed to control the direction of flow. In pneumatics, this switch is called a directional control valve (DCV). Almost every pneumatic circuit uses one or more pneumatic DCVs.

One common type of DCV is a 4-way, 3-position DCV. This is the type used in the Amatrol 85-BP Basic Pneumatic trainer, as shown in figure 53. Applications use 4-way, 3-position DCVs to provide 3-function control of the actuator: extend, retract, and stop in mid-position.

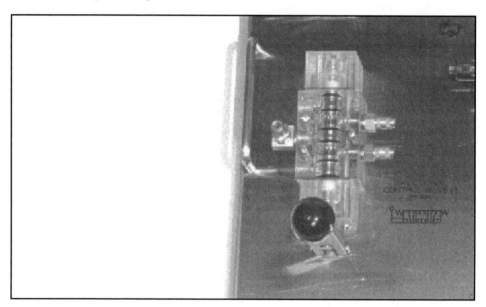

Figure 53. 850 Series 4-Way, 3-Position Directional Control Valve

The 4-way, 3-position pneumatic DCV, shown is figure 54, consists of four components:

- **Valve Body -** The valve body provides the passageway for the sliding spool. It has five ports drilled into it which provide flow paths for the air. Pneumatic DCV bodies are often made of cast aluminum because the pressures are low. The 4-way, 3-position DCV valve body on the Amatrol trainer is made from clear plastic to allow visual observation of the valve operation.
- **Spool -** The spool is the "switch" of the valve. It slides back and forth in the body to channel the flow through to specific ports. The spool, shown in figure 54, has grooves which can allow air to flow past the o-ring seals inside the body when the spool is shifted.
- **Operator -** The operator is the mechanism that moves the spool from one position to another. Examples of operators used to shift pneumatic DCVs include the lever, manual palm button, solenoid (electrical operator), and pneumatic operator.
- **Springs -** A 3-position valve usually has a main spring on either side of the spool to position it in the middle when the operator is not energized.

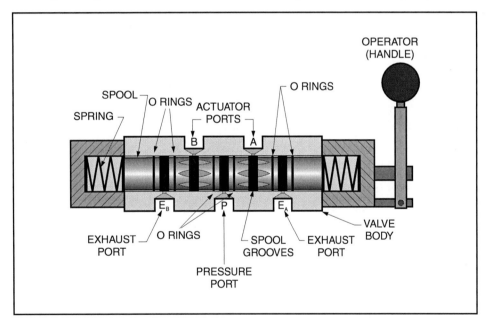

Figure 54. Main Components of a 4-Way, 3-Position DCV

Notice in figure 54 that the ports are labeled. The P is for the pressure, or inlet, port. E_A and E_B are used to label the exhaust ports. There are also two actuator ports labeled A and B. These are usually connected to the lines going to the cylinder or motor. They allow air flow to and from the actuator.

Directional control valves are manufactured in many different styles and sizes with a wide variety of options. One major classification of directional control valves is by the number of flow paths, or ways, available for air to flow through a particular valve. Pneumatic DCVs are available as one-way, two-way, three-way, four-way, and four-way types.

In addition to classifying valves by the number of ways, a valve can also be classified by the number of positions to which it can be adjusted. A position determines which ports are connected to each other. Industrial pneumatic DCVs are most often supplied as either 2-position or 3-position types. The type explored in this LAP is a 3-position type.

As a shortcut, DCV ways and positions are commonly stated together by using two numbers separated by a slash, such as 3/2, 4/3, etc. The first number is the number of ways and the second is the number of positions. As an example, a 3/2 DCV is a 3-way, 2-position directional control valve.

The schematic symbols for DCVs use what is called a flow envelope to show the state of the flow paths for each valve spool position. These flow paths can be shown as either opened or closed by the envelope, as shown in figure 55.

NOTE

In the fluid power industry, the terms open and closed mean just the opposite of the meaning in the electrical industry. An electrical switch passes electricity when it is closed. A fluidpower valve passes fluid when it is open.

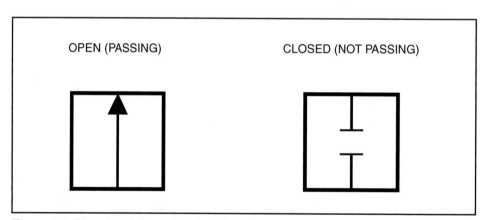

Figure 55. Directional Control Valve Flow Envelopes

The flow envelopes of figure 55 represent two different flow conditions of a 2-way DCV symbol. A complete 2-way, 2-position (2/2) DCV symbol combines these two flow envelopes, as shown in figure 56. In one spool position, the valve passes flow between its two ports. In the other position, the ports are blocked.

To determine when the spool is in a particular position, operators are placed next to each envelope. In figure 56, a spring is placed next to the passing flow envelope. This means that the de-energized flow condition is passing. The lever operator next to the blocked flow envelope shows the flow condition when the lever is operated (valve is energized). In this case, it is a blocked condition.

The complete description of the symbol shown in figure 56 is a manually-operated, spring return, 2-way, 2-position, normally passing DCV.

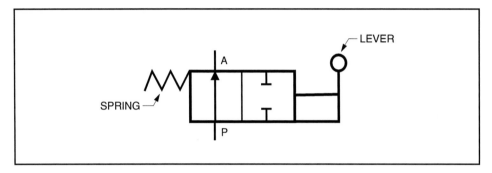

Figure 56. 2-Way, 2-Position (2/2) DCV Symbol

A 4-way DCV symbol has two flow paths per envelope which show the connections between its five ports (P, A, B, E_A and E_B). If the valve has two positions, two flow envelopes are drawn side by side, as shown in figure 57. Each envelope shows the flow path condition for a particular position of the spool. The two exhaust ports are considered just one way because they perform the same function.

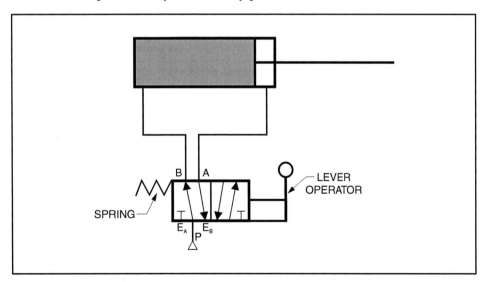

Figure 57. 4-Way, 2-Position (4/2) DCV Schematic Symbol

Figure 58 shows the condition of the 4-way DCV when its lever is actuated. The spool moves to the condition where air flows from P to A, retracting the cylinder. When the lever is released, the spring pushes the spool to the condition where air flows from P to B, causing the cylinder to extend.

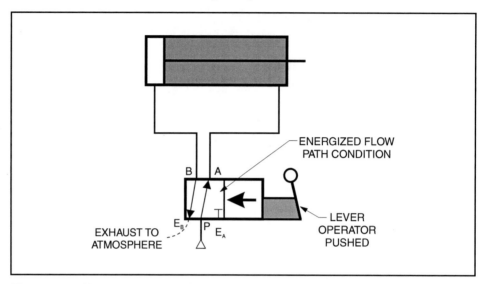

Figure 58. 4-Way, 2-Position (4/2) DCV Energized

The schematic symbol for a 3-position valve adds one more flow envelope and a second spring, as shown in figure 59. The details of the operation will be explained further in the skill.

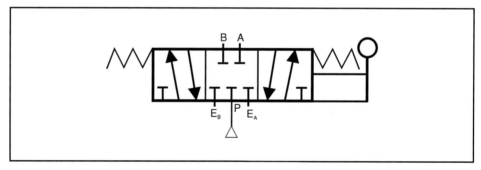

Figure 59. 4-Way, 3-Position (4/3) Pneumatic DCV Schematic Symbol

Procedure Overview

In this procedure, you will set up a basic pneumatic circuit to reciprocate a cylinder using a 4-way, 3-position directional control valve. You will find that this method is much easier than switching hose connections as you did in an earlier skill.

❑ 1. Connect the pneumatic circuit shown in figure 60 on the 850 Series pneumatic trainer.

NOTE

Make sure all your hose connections are firmly made.

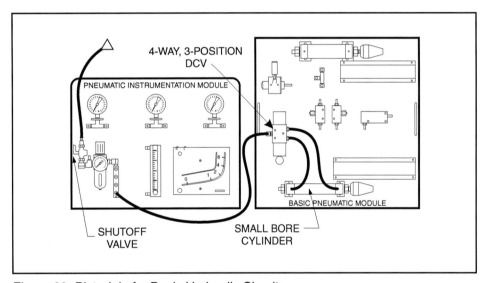

Figure 60. Pictorial of a Basic Hydraulic Circuit

❏ 2. Now look at the schematic diagram shown in figure 61. Compare this with the actual hose connections shown in figure 60.

As you can see, the hose connections are drawn to the center flow envelope, which is the normal or de-energized condition. The normal position of a 3-position valve is almost always designed to be the center condition because the two springs center the spool.

Being a control valve, the DCV is usually located between the regulator and the actuator.

NOTE

A 4-way DCV is the type needed to extend and retract a double-acting cylinder. A 4-way DCV with 3-positions is used if the cylinder must stop in mid-position.

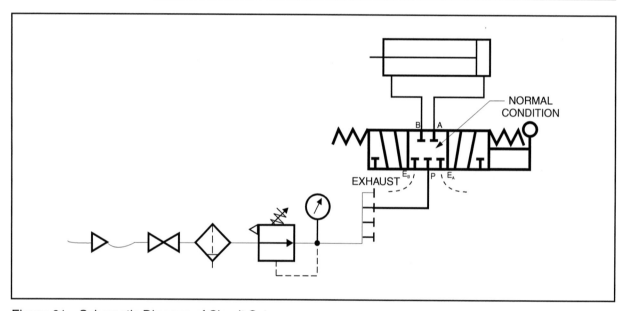

Figure 61.   Schematic Diagram of Circuit Setup

❏ 3. Perform the following substeps to connect the compressed air supply.

A. If not already connected, connect the compressed air supply source to the male quick-connect plug on the instrumentation module.

B. Open the shutoff valve.

❑ 4. Turn the regulator adjustment knob CW until the pressure at the regulator gauge reads 20 psi / 138 kPa.

You should see that the cylinder does not move even though the pressure has been raised. With the lever handle released, as shown in figure 62, the valve spool is held in the mid-position by the springs. The spool blocks flow at all ports because the o-rings seal each port from the others. This holds the actuator stopped.

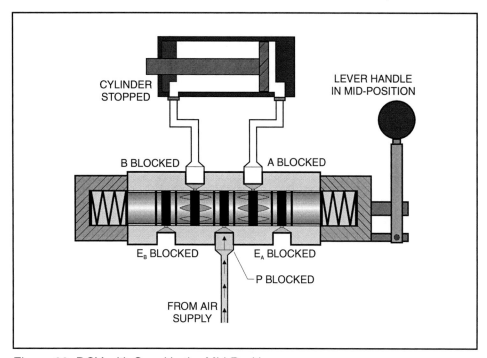

Figure 62. DCV with Spool in the Mid-Position

❑ 5. Now test your pneumatic circuit by pushing in on the lever of the DCV to extend the cylinder's rod. Continue holding the lever until the cylinder's rod is fully extended. Then release it.

When the manual lever is placed (pushed) in towards the body, the grooves in the spool allow air to flow from one port to another. In this case, the spool is shifted to connect Port P with Port A, and Port B with the exhaust port (E_B).

As shown in figures 63 and 64, air flow through the valve is P to A, and from B to E_B. This causes the cylinder to extend with the air from B exhausted out through E_B into the atmosphere.

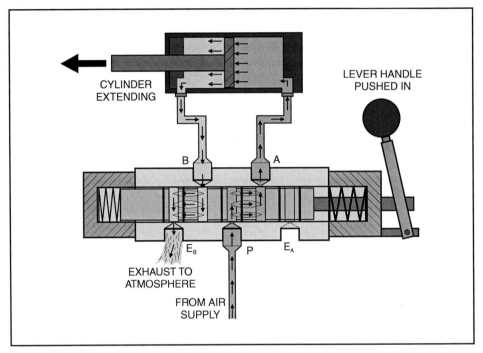

Figure 63. DCV with Spool Shifted P to A and B to E_B

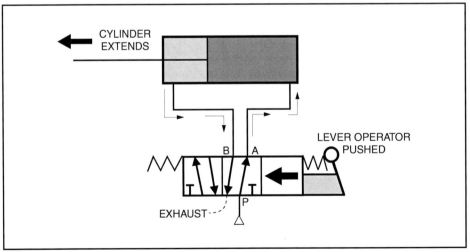

Figure 64. Schematic of DCV Shifted to P-to-A Condition

❑ 6. Retract the cylinder by pulling out on the lever of the directional control valve. Continue holding until the cylinder's rod is fully retracted. Then release it.

When the lever is placed (pulled) away from the body, the grooves in the spool are shifted in a direction that causes a different set of ports to be connected. In this case, the spool is shifted to connect Port P with Port B, and Port A with the exhaust port (E_A), as shown in figures 65 and 66. This causes the cylinder to retract with air from A exhausted out E_A into the atmosphere.

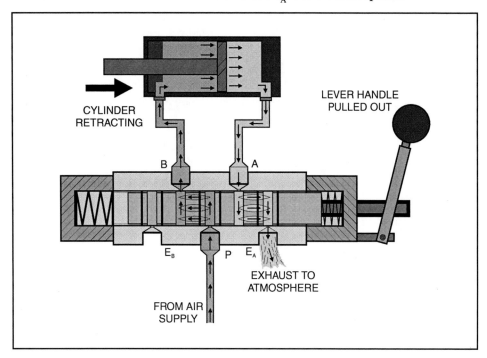

Figure 65. DCV with Spool Shifted P to B and A to E_A

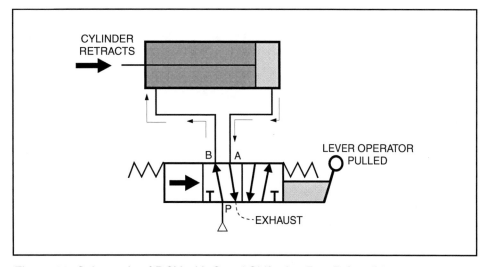

Figure 66. Schematic of DCV with Spool Shifted to P to B Condition

❑ 7. Repeat steps 5 and 6 several times to cycle the cylinder. During one of the cycles, release the lever while the cylinder's rod is extending and in mid-stroke. What happens? Does the cylinder stop or does the rod keep moving?

_____

_____

You should observe that the cylinder stops in mid-stroke because the spool moves to the center position and blocks the ports. This is one of the functions for which you should choose a 3-position valve.

❑ 8. Turn the regulator adjustment CCW fully to reduce the pressure to a minimum.

❑ 9. Close the shutoff valve.

❑ 10. Move the lever of the DCV back and forth to remove any pressure still in the circuit.

This circuit will have pressure trapped between the valve and the cylinder after normal operation because the DCV blocks all ports in the mid-position.

❑ 11. Switch the two hoses connected to the ports of the cylinder with each other so the cap end is connected to Port B of the DCV and the rod end is connected to Port A of the DCV.

❑ 12. Open the shutoff valve.

❑ 13. Turn the regulator adjustment knob CW until the pressure at the regulator gauge reads 20 psi / 138 kPa.

❑ 14. Cycle the cylinder again by operating the DCV. What difference do you observe in how the system operates?

_____

_____

You should observe that the cylinder moves in the opposite direction when the lever is pushed in. This step shows that the direction of the cylinder's motion depends not only on the internal porting of the DCV but also how the DCV and cylinder are connected. The cylinder motion can easily be changed by switching hoses. This is a common task performed in industry.

❑ 15. Turn the regulator adjustment CCW fully to reduce the pressure to a minimum.

❑ 16. Close the shutoff valve.

❑ 17. Move the lever of the DCV back and forth to remove any pressure still in the circuit.

❑ 18. Disconnect and store hoses.

Procedure Overview

In this procedure, you will further develop your understanding of pneumatic circuits by designing two basic circuits.

□ 1. Read the following scenario.

Scenario: Your company has asked you to design an automated system that uses a conveyor to move the product into and out of the oven.

To keep from losing heat, you have decided to use lift gates that open only when the product is about to enter or leave the oven. To power these gates, pneumatic cylinders are used, as shown in figure 67.

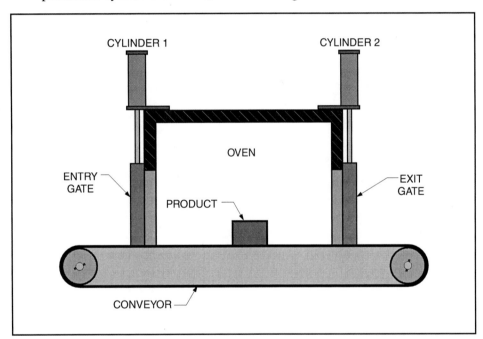

Figure 67. Automated Oven

❑ 2. Your task is to design a pneumatic circuit that will cause the cylinders to extend and retract using separate directional control valves. Each valve should provide extend, retract, and mid-position stop capability.

Draw the circuit schematic using the symbols you have learned in this LAP. Start your drawing from the air supply, as shown in figure 68. Include a regulator and filter. Remember, schematics are drawn with the components in the de-energized condition.

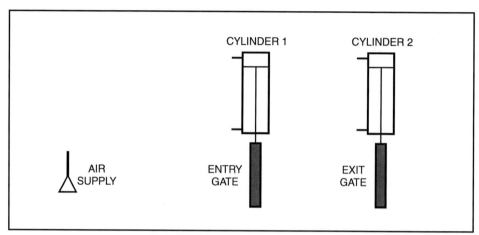

Figure 68. Schematic of Circuit Design

❑ 3. Now add pressure gauges to your design to measure the system pressure and the pressures at the cap and rod ends of the cylinder.

❑ 4. Read this scenario.

Scenario: An automatic wash booth, as shown in figure 69, uses a conveyor to move parts sequentially through the washer. The sequence is:

A. Open both doors at the same time.

B. With doors open, the conveyor runs, moving the clean part out of the booth and putting the part to be cleaned into the booth.

C. With the part to be cleaned positioned in the booth, the conveyor stops and both doors close.

D. The part is washed and dried.

E. The sequence is repeated.

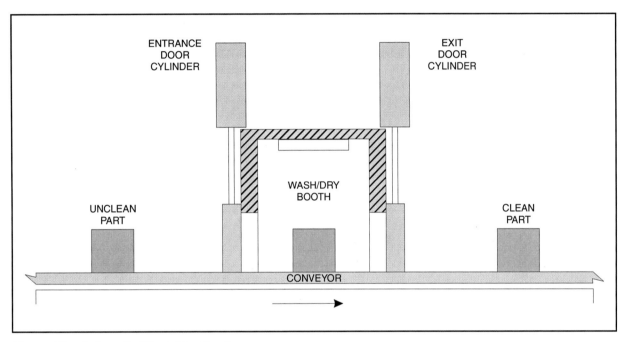

Figure 69. Automatic Wash/Dry Booth

❑ 5. Your task is to design a pneumatic circuit that will cause the door cylinders to operate together, using the same DCV. Door operation must have stop capability in case of emergency.

Draw the circuit schematic, using the symbols you learned in this LAP. Start your drawing from the air supply, as shown in figure 70. Include a combination filter-regulator-gauge unit.

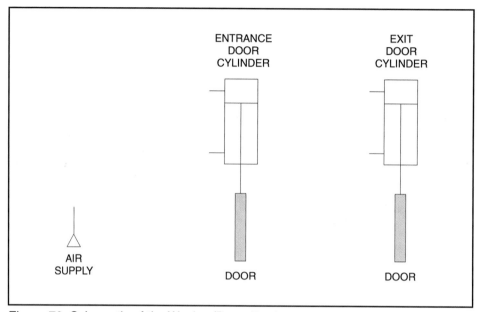

Figure 70. Schematic of the Washer/Dryer Design

❑ 6. Using the Amatrol 85-BP Training System, connect the circuit you designed.

❑ 7. Connect the compressed air supply to the male quick-connect on the instrumentation module and open the shutoff valve.

❑ 8. Adjust the regulator to 20 psi/78 kPa.

❑ 9. Verify that the cylinders extend and retract together.

Because of the difference in size, one cylinder will move before the other. Your design is correct if both cylinders extend with a single shift of the DCV, both retract with a single shift of the DCV and the cylinder action can be stopped mid-stroke by centering the DCV.

❑10. With both cylinders retracted, reduce the regulator pressure to minimum by turning the adjustment knob CCW fully.

❑11. Close the shutoff valve.

❑12. Move the handle of the DCV back and forth to remove all pressure from the circuit.

❑13. Disconnect and store hoses.

1. The actuator that produces linear motion is called a(n) _____.

2. The number of ways that a directional control valve has defines the number of _____ paths for the fluid to travel through the valve.

3. Four methods used to shift (move) a DCV spool are manual palm button, _____, _____, and pneumatic.

4. Double-acting cylinder direction can be reversed by switching the hose connections at the _____ or at the _____.

5. The type of cylinder that needs to be powered in both directions is called a(n) _____ cylinder.

6. The spool of a 3-position DCV is held in the middle position by a(n) _____.

7. The four-way, 3-position pneumatic DCV components are valve body, operator, springs, and _____.

8. A 4/3 DCV has _____ ways and _____ positions.